£5.95 £8.80

CONTEI

Where's the answers?

Can you see my scars, can you see them?
Do you know my feelings, do you know them?
Can you feel the pain, can you feel it?
Do you know my shame - was I to blame?

Shaz

INTRODUCTION

The idea for this book came from people who self-harm, and who wanted something they could use to help them to understand themselves better and to have more choices about how they cope with their lives and feelings.

Many people who have struggled with self-harm have developed new ways of dealing with their feelings and experiences. All of the self-help ideas in this book have come from them, and are offered to others who are making this difficult journey, in the hope that they may be helpful.

This book is not about trying to stop people from self-harming. No-one has the right to do that. But many people would like to have more choices about how to cope. This book aims to help increase those choices.

We are often asked whether it is possible for someone to stop self-harming. Not everyone wants to give up self-harm. Some people are satisfied with self-harm as a way of getting by. Others are not happy about it and want to stop. For those who wish to stop it is possible to do so but it will take time and patience. You will need to build up your understanding of what lies behind your self-harm, and find ways of dealing with those experiences and difficulties. This book aims to equip you with some of the tools you need to do this. Then you will be freer to choose.

We know of many people who have stopped self-harming, some after many years of coping in this way. But whether or not you wish to stop, we would like to hold out the hope of easing the terrible pain that leads to self-harm.

HOW TO USE THIS BOOK

You may wish to read this book from cover to cover, and at other times you may want help with something specific. We have tried to arrange the book in such a way as to make it quick and easy for you to find what you want.

The first section explains some of the reasons why people self-harm and what makes a person vulnerable to doing so. It also sets out to help you explore the reasons why *you* self-harm.

Next comes the biggest part of the book. Each section looks in turn at one of the ways self-harm may help people cope. There are suggestions for new ways in which you can express yourself and meet your needs. The last section is about building up good feelings about yourself and your body, enriching your life and getting support for yourself.

Each section consists of some talking about the subject, followed by some self-help ideas you can try (these are in single line boxes). These involve things like writing, or saying things onto a tape, and drawing. This might seem a bit daunting but remember it's not about producing works of art. It's about exploring and expressing things for yourself. Odd words and stick drawings can do the job. You will find quotes, poems and drawings from other people who have worked on their self-harm and feelings, which we hope will encourage and inspire you.

Do use the book how you want to, homing in on what feels useful to you at any particular time. We hope it will help you on your own particular journey.

UNDERSTANDING SELF-HARM

In this book, we use the term 'self-harm' to mean any ways in which someone might injure, hurt or harm themselves, as a way of coping with unbearable distress. Most of the time these sorts of self-harm are carried out **not** with the intention of suicide, but on the contrary, as a way of making life bearable, to be able to go on. However, sometimes a person's despair is so great that they do wish to die. And sometimes people self-harm without being quite clear what their intention is - they just feel desperate and driven to *do something* to themselves.

The sorts of self-harm we are concentrating on here are part of a wide range of harmful things people do to cope, such as drinking, smoking, over-working, troubled eating, etc. Many of the ideas in the book are relevant to them too.

For someone who injures or harms themselves repeatedly, there are usually both long term and short term reasons. They may hurt themselves when difficult things happen in their lives right now, but there are often also underlying, longer-term reasons for what they feel and do.

The origins of self-harm often lie in distressing experiences or circumstances which the person has suffered in the past. Often some sort of loss or trauma is involved. Usually, but not always, some of these painful things happened in the person's childhood or teenage years. Other distressing things may also have happened to them as adults.

These events will have caused the person more pain than they could cope with at that time. The experiences may also have made it hard for them to feel good about themselves, to express their feelings and to feel confident in relationships with other people.

The person is then left with a backlog of struggle and pain which don't go away, even though they may be hidden beneath a competent, cheerful exterior. The events of the past may be over, but the anguish remains and sometimes wells up unbearably, until the person resorts to hurting themselves to release or escape from their feelings.

Furthermore, when any difficult or upsetting things happen in their day to day lives, the person is in trouble. The upset of the current situation is added to the pile of hurt and distress inside. Yet again it feels hard to cope, to understand and express the awful feelings, or to hold on to any self-esteem. So the person resorts to harming themselves. To others (and perhaps to themselves) it seems like the self-harm has been caused by the present situation alone. That can be very difficult if the situation seems a bit trivial, or if it involves another person (for example if someone self-harms following a row). But in reality, the current situation is often more distressing and difficult because of the effects of past experiences. The self-harm is a response *both* to the thing which has just happened (the short term reason or 'trigger'), *and* to the anguish and difficulties set up by past experiences.

It is fitting that we sometimes use the word 'trigger' to refer to some of the things which can make a person feel like harming themselves on any particular day. It might be quite a smallish thing which causes the trigger to be pulled. But the 'gun' has been loaded previously by the big and painful things which have happened to the person.

4

EXPERIENCES UNDERLYING SELF-HARM

The sorts of experiences which often underlie self-harm are those which have caused a person a lot of pain. Often they have also made the person feel 'bad' and powerless. Some of the sorts of experiences often involved include:

Abuse and violence

A lot of people who self-harm (but by no means all) were abused in some way as children. They may have been physically hurt and maltreated, or sexually interfered with or exploited. (Sexual abuse doesn't necessarily involve rape or even touching, it can also include anything which makes the child feel uncomfortable, confused and intruded upon.)

Much of the abuse which children and young people suffer happens in their homes, or comes from other adults they know. However, bullying and assaults by other children can also cause great distress which may lead to self-harm.

Abuse, violence and bullying also happens to adults, and some people (more often women) self-harm after being sexually assaulted or harassed, or following violence by a partner. Some people suffer intolerable harassment, hatred and abuse motivated by racism or homophobia.

These sorts of experiences are terrifying, traumatic and confusing. They can leave a person feeling bad and guilty (even though *they* have done nothing wrong), as well as betrayed, helpless, devastated and full of grief and pain. This powerful cocktail of feelings often leads people to a desperate search for ways of alleviating and expressing their suffering, including a wide range of self-harm.

Neglect, deprivation and emotional abuse

Some people who self-harm were physically neglected as children. Perhaps more were emotionally deprived. This means not being adequately loved, comforted, hugged, praised and supported as a child needs. It may be that the adults around them were not able to give these things (perhaps because of their own difficulties). Nonetheless, someone who does not receive enough emotional or physical care and support as a child can be left with a terrible legacy of pain, emptiness, and lack of confidence. They have also not had the chance to learn how to care for and comfort themselves.

Emotional abuse is very wide and harder to define than physical abuse. However, its effects can be just as devastating. It can include many things which make the child feel confused, tormented, frightened, abandoned, overwhelmed, worthless, or responsible for things which are just too much for them.

Some children are emotionally abused by being put down, ridiculed and criticised, or shouted at a lot. Perhaps too much is expected of them, in various ways. For many children, emotional abuse comes from being forced to be involved in adults' problems. For example, children may repeatedly see parents arguing and fighting, and may be pulled into the rows as 'weapon', ally or peacemaker. Some children are made to feel to blame for things that go wrong in the home, or responsible for their parents' own distress and misery. Often emotional abuse occurs because the lives and relationships of the adults around are painful and chaotic. Some of this pain and chaos is dumped upon the child, who is too young and vulnerable to deal with it.

Emotional abuse and deprivation can also happen in adult relationships. Adults may have more choice about their partners than children do about their parents or carers. However, adults can still become trapped in a relationship with someone who emotionally mistreats, manipulates or exploits them, while giving them little or no support and love. Gradually this undermines their confidence, making them feel confused, lonely, desperate, and perhaps believing they are at fault.

Loss and bereavement

For some people, self-harm follows the loss of someone very important to them. Some children and teenagers begin to self-harm after one of their parents, grandparents, brothers or sisters dies, or perhaps when they lose parents through separation. The pain caused by losses such as these may be more than the child can bear, especially if they are not given enough comfort in their loss, and support to grieve as they need to.

Adults may also self-harm when they lose someone, either through bereavement or the break-up of a relationship. The losses brought by events such as a miscarriage, unemployment, illness or disability or other major life change or trauma may also lead someone to cope by self-harming. Adults may also harm themselves as a way of dealing with the left-over pain of childhood losses.

Loss is part of everyone's life, but for someone who has been made particularly vulnerable by losses or difficulties in childhood, or who doesn't have enough support to bear their grief, self-harm may be the only means by which they can express or escape their anguish.

Isolation and lack of communication and support

Many people who self-harm seem to have been very isolated and unsupported. Often their self-harm seems to originate from circumstances where they could not share and communicate their feelings and experiences. Children may be isolated because their family or carers do not talk with them and listen to them, especially about feelings, thoughts and problems. Some children are isolated and unable to communicate because of disabilities or language difficulties. Families may be very isolated because of alcoholism, illness, financial difficulties, and so on. Children who are being abused at home are often deliberately isolated and made to be secretive by abusers.

Youngsters and adults may be lonely and isolated if they are not accepted and supported by the community in which they live, for example due to racism, homophobia or other discrimination. For various reasons, adults can find themselves lonely and with few opportunities to communicate their difficulties and feelings. A partner may not want to listen to them, yet be jealous and prevent them from having any other friendships. Or they may be isolated following the loss of a partner. Domestic violence isolates women and children. Experiences such as being stuck at home with young children, unemployment, homelessness, illness, going to prison and so on also often lead people to feel very isolated and out of touch with others.

Where people cannot talk about their problems or gain support for their distress from others, self-harm may become a powerful way in which to express themselves and manage the feelings which threaten to overwhelm them.

HOW SELF-HARM HELPS PEOPLE COPE

We have seen that self-harm is a way of coping with overwhelming feelings that result from awful experiences. But how does it achieve this? There are lots of ways self-harm seems to 'work' and it can be different for different people or at different times. Here are some of them. We will be looking at these in greater detail in the section on finding other ways.

Feeling anguish and pain - *acknowledging, expressing or distracting oneself from painful feelings*

Needing to take some control - *giving a sense of control over something in one's life*

Exploding with anger - *expressing or defusing angry feelings*

Feeling guilt and shame - *dealing with feelings of guilt, shame and self-hatred*

Feeling empty and needy - *trying to fill the emptiness inside and gain some comfort*

It's who you are - *a way of saying 'this is me'*

Feeling unreal or panicky - *a way of 'bringing oneself back' from frightening panic or numbness*

Sending a message - *letting others know how you feel when words seem useless*

You may recognise that self-harm works in some of these ways for you. It is great that you have found some way of coping. Self-harm may even have saved your life in the past. You may feel that self-harm has been a necessary friend to you. But you may also feel it has become a tyrant which you cannot do without even if you would like to. The important point here is that the things you get from self-harm are things that you need and are entitled to. How you get them is down to you, but what the rest of this book aims to do is to offer you a wider choice of ways to express yourself and meet your needs.

My old friend

Pain overwhelms
and possesses my body
my heart freezes up
with fear and despair.
My voice is locked in
and my hands are shaking
I cannot let out
my torment here.
When I get home
I'll turn to my old friend
hoping the blade
will release me from pain.
But my shame and disgust
will exact retribution
for seeking this comfort
again and again.   *Kim.*

EXPLORING YOUR OWN SELF-HARM

The reasons why you self-harm are special and unique to you. They may include some of those mentioned in the last section, but this does not include everything that can lead someone to self-harm. You might not be sure why you self-harm or you may already be aware of some of the reasons but want to explore it further.

WHAT SELF-HARM IS ABOUT FOR ME

Get a large piece of paper and some coloured pencils or pens. In the middle of the page write the words 'SELF-HARM' (or whatever words you prefer, like 'cutting-up' or 'over-dosing').

Around this write any words that come to mind which seem to be associated with it. They could be words about feelings, about your life and the things that have happened to you, people in your life past or present - anything that to you seems to be associated with self-harm. Choose colours that seem right for the words or draw pictures if you like.

When you've run out of ideas sit back and look at what you have written. (Or you could come back to it later.) Are there any surprises? What does it tell you about things from the past that may still be affecting how you feel? What does it tell you about things in your life now which may be causing you distress? Can you see what sorts of feelings drive you to self-harm?

EXPLORING THE PAST

It can be helpful to explore for yourself what particular things in your life in the past have caused you pain and perhaps led you to self-harm. You don't have to do this all at once - only as much as you want, at your own pace.

TELLING YOUR LIFE STORY

One good way of exploring and recording things about your life is in the form of a scrap book (or you could use a loose-leaf file). Into this you put things like photographs, letters, school reports, drawings, certificates, and mementoes of any sort. You also include anything you would like to write about the past. (If you prefer to talk, rather than write, you could record yourself talking about things onto a tape.)

It can be helpful to start by doing a quick time-line or list, showing what things have happened to you and when. This will help you identify important things you want to explore in depth, when you are ready to.

The sorts of things to write, talk or draw about are events, situations, people, etc. which seem significant *to you*. Just pick one thing at a time that you feel you'd like to explore, and tell the story of it, including your feelings - then and now. You could include something about when you started to self-harm, and how that developed. What you say can be long or short - whatever conveys your experience. You don't have to talk about things in the right order - later you can organise your scrap book or file to tell your story in a particular order, if you want.

This exercise is something you can keep doing over time, adding to your scrap book whenever you want. You can look back over it to help you see your own suffering and understand your own difficulties better. It could also be good to show what you have done to someone else who is interested and supportive.

Whatever your experiences, it is possible for you to get over the pain of the past and its effects on you. This needs to happen in its own time, in ways that are right for you. Often part of the process involves talking with other people about your experiences and feelings, when you are ready to. This can include friends and partners, support groups, a counsellor or therapist - people who take you seriously and support you in exploring your needs and feelings.

There are also things you can do on your own, and books can help. The 'Telling Your Story' exercise above and some other ideas in this book are designed to help you to understand the pain you feel and how it may relate to the past. There are also ideas for things to do to help you deal with the difficult feelings the past has left you with, which is in itself an important part of resolving painful past experiences. A lot of what this book is about is helping you to change some of the ways in which the past may have affected you in your life now. We hope some of the ideas will help you to feel better about yourself and happier with who you are.

EXPLORING YOUR CURRENT LIFE

There may be things in your life now that underlie your self-harm. This may be on top of things in your past, or your self-harm may be all to do with your life now. It can be hard to look at your life now in an objective way because you are right in the middle of it. But there are ways of gaining some distance in order to see what is going on.

ME AND MY LIFE

Collect together a lot of small items that you are familiar with. These can be anything, such as keys, pens, rings, small ornaments, etc. Go through your pockets or bag or look round the room and see what you come up with.

Now choose one of them to represent yourself and place it in front of you. You can use a table or the floor. One by one choose other items to represent people and things in your life , and place them where you think they should go in relation to you. Keep shifting things around until you have your current life represented in front of you.

When you are satisfied with it look to see which things you have placed close and which further away. How does it feel? Do you like how things are? Is there anything about it that is uncomfortable or upsetting?

When you feel you have learnt all you can from this representation, try moving things around to positions which feel better. You can remove some items altogether if you wish, or add new ones. Keep going until you are satisfied this is how you would like your life to be.

This exercise can tell you a lot about what is right and what is wrong in your life. It can also help you to see what changes you might need to make, or at least aim for.

Sometimes someone can be very unhappy, but not ready to change big things in their life. Even thinking about change can be scary. It is helpful to say to yourself "I don't have to change anything". You can *think* about what is wrong in your life, and know that when you are ready, you will be able to make it different. In the meantime, you could do some very small, safe things to make your daily life a bit better.

VULNERABLE TIMES

Whatever the underlying reasons for self-harm, at certain times you can be particularly vulnerable. You may feel more distressed and less able to cope without hurting yourself. At the time, though, you may not realise why you are feeling quite so fragile, and may give yourself a hard time about it. Vulnerable times can include:

- When you are tired, hungry, stressed or not very well. Being physically under par makes it harder to support yourself emotionally.

- Certain times of day - perhaps evenings or night times - that are particularly hard for you.

- Certain times of the week - often weekends are hard.

- Before or during a menstrual period.

- At difficult times of year (such as Christmas), or around anniversaries of painful or significant events.

- At times of change, such as moving home, changing job, leaving school or college, etc.

- When you are away from your usual supports - people, familiar things; even when you're on holiday.

It can be very useful to keep a diary or chart showing your feelings, events in your life, and times when you self-harm. Over time this can help you see when you are most vulnerable. At those times you need to make allowances for yourself and take extra care of yourself . You might also need to get some extra support to help you cope.

FINDING OTHER WAYS

WHEN YOU DON'T KNOW WHY

In this book we talk a lot about understanding *why* you self-harm. However, the reality is that often people simply feel a compelling urge to hurt themselves. They don't know why. They just know that they feel awful and that somehow harming themselves will help. In this section we will look at some things you can do when you feel like self-harming, don't really know why, but don't know what else to do. This has two purposes. First, to help you understand yourself and your self-harm more. Second, to give you some more options about what to do, should you want them.

THIS IS WHAT I'M SAYING

For many people it seems like self-harm is a kind of 'language', in which they express important things. One thing which can help you to understand your self-harm and have more choices about it is to try to work out what you might be 'saying' when you hurt yourself.

You can do this on your own or with someone else. It's a good idea to record your ideas on paper or on a cassette tape, so you've got them later to remind you. What you do, is to ask yourself the question:

If I self-harmed now, what might I be saying?

Then write down or say out loud anything which comes into your mind. Don't 'censor' it. Don't think you've got to get one 'right' answer. There are probably lots of answers.

17

The last exercise might give you some ideas about things you need, or feelings that need expressing, changes you might want to make in your life, and so on. You can do the exercise at any time, if you want to try to understand yourself and your self-harm better, as well as at particular moments when you have the urge to self-harm.

A WOUND ON PAPER

If what you want to do is injure yourself in some way, a good idea is to get some paper and draw on that the marks or wounds you want to make. You can just draw the wound, or draw your body (or part of it) with the injuries you feel like making shown on it. It can be good to draw or paint it big, in colour.

Next, write down any words that feel right, alongside the injuries you have drawn. Just write what comes, odd words and phrases, it doesn't have to make sense. You might feel like drawing some other things too. Use any colours that you want. Just keep going until you feel you've run out of things to put.

Now sit back and look at what you have drawn and written. Notice what messages there are in what you have written. It might be sad or shocking, but also quite satisfying to look at. You may be upset, and it's important to take care of yourself - say some comforting things to yourself. Perhaps you'll find that you don't need to actually hurt yourself any longer, having drawn and understood what you felt like doing to yourself.

You could also show what you have drawn to someone else who will understand and take it seriously.

THINGS TO REMIND YOURSELF OF

If I feel like self-harming it's because there is **something wrong** which deserves attention.

It's okay to be confused. It's all right not to know why. I can take my time to gradually understand myself more.

My feelings, whatever they are, are real and important.

FEELING ANGUISH AND PAIN

For many people, self-harm is first and foremost a way in which they try to deal with the terrible feelings of hurt, pain, grief and despair which overwhelm them. Sometimes it seems like doing harm to oneself is the only way of *acknowledging* just how much hurt and sorrow you carry inside. Hurting oneself can be a way of *expressing* the pain - some people have called self-harm 'a silent scream'. Sometimes hurting yourself, taking tablets, etc., is a way of trying to *get away from* the awful feelings. In this section we will look in turn at ways of doing these important things: acknowledging the hurts inside, expressing feelings, soothing, and giving yourself some respite from the pain.

ACKNOWLEDGING THE FEELINGS

One of the hardest things about emotional injuries and pain is that they are invisible. It can be hard to take your own pain and suffering seriously, or to communicate to others how much you're hurting inside. The pain doesn't show and those around you may not even know that anything is wrong. Hurting your body may be a way of saying "this is how much I hurt" or "something's wrong, please help me".

What self-harm seems to have particular power to do is to show *on our bodies* that we are hurt. The wound, mark (or perhaps thinness or illness) can seem to stand for the emotional hurts inside. If you are suffering, you need acknowledgement of your feelings from yourself and others. You might be able to find new ways of getting that.

AN 'IMAGE' OF SUFFERING

One powerful thing to do is to make an image of your body, and show on it the injuries and damage which you feel you have suffered. You could do this as a picture or a model.

If you prefer to draw or paint, get some of the right sort of paper for your image - big or small, white, black, red, and so on. Have some different coloured pens/crayons/paints handy so you can use whatever seems right as you go on. You don't have to draw yourself your real colour. Green, purple, etc. might seem more like your image of pain. You could make a figure with something like coloured plasticine or modelling dough. Clay can be painted when it is dry. Get together some things you can use to mark the model.

Draw or make a simple outline of your body as **you** feel it to be. If you feel very young, you can draw or make a child or baby figure. If your experiences have made you feel really old and frail, show that. If you feel deprived and starved, you could draw or model yourself very thin. If you feel broken or tortured and twisted out of shape by what has happened to you, make your image like that. Next mark on the figure any wounds you feel are needed to show what has happened to you and the pain you feel.

Try to look with respect and compassion at what you have made or drawn. Be kind to yourself if you feel upset to see your pain shown in this way. Decide what to do next with your image - to put it away gently in a safe place, to show it to someone who cares, or to change it in some way. You could also do something like lighting a candle for the hurt self you have shown.

21

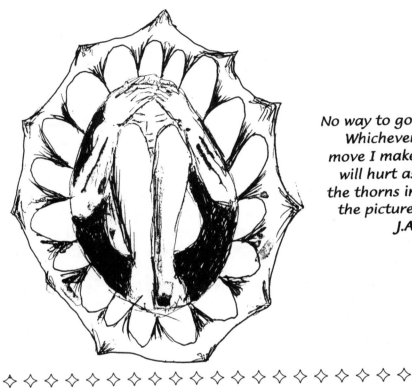

No way to go.
Whichever
move I make
will hurt as
the thorns in
the picture.
J.A.

I HURT

Write down all the things your self-harm might be telling someone who could help. They might be things about how you are feeling, or things about what has happened to you. They might just be words, like 'help' or 'stop'. You might want to show (or send) what you have written to someone who will understand or be able to help you.

Another thing you might do is to say the words aloud when you are alone. Just to say "I hurt", "I'm desperate", or whatever it is you need to say can be a relief.

EXPRESSING THE FEELINGS

Pain and grief **need** expression. You might not be able to change what has happened in your life to hurt you. But letting out the awful anguish that you feel can help to ease the pain and relieve despair. Putting it on the outside can make it more bearable. Often people who self-harm say they find it difficult to cry, or to say in words to others what they feel. Sometimes the blood from cutting themselves seems to represent the tears they cannot shed. Perhaps the wound is like a 'mouth' which can 'speak' for them.

We can express and honour our pain in many, many ways. Even if it's hard to cry, you can do things to recognise your feelings and give them the expression they need and deserve. You could explore some new ways which suit you. Take it slowly, just letting yourself feel and express what you can manage at any time. With all of the ideas which follow, remember to comfort yourself for your pain.

SCREAMING THE PAIN

Sometimes the pain can feel like a scream inside you. Letting out a scream can be very difficult (especially when you have neighbours). You could try playing some loud music while you do it. Screaming into a cushion might help.

Try at first just to make any sound, then again and again, working it up into a scream. Imagine all the pain and anguish pouring out with the scream. You may find you end up crying. Let the pain flow out through the tears too.

I'm going to SCREAM

I'm going to SCREAM
But who gives a shit?
You say that you care
But that's about it.

How can things be right
When everything's wrong?
You say that I'll cope
But I'm not that strong.

You say you can help
You say you will stay
You say I'll be fine
But I can't live this way.

I need you to be there
For me all the time
Not just when I'm normal
Is that such a crime?

I need you to tell me
That I'm not that bad
I need you to tell me
I'm not going mad
I need you to tell me
That you will be strong
I need you beside me
When it all goes so wrong.

I'm going to SCREAM
But who gives a shit?
You all say that you care
But that's about it.   **by C.**

24

DRAWING THE PAIN

Imagine your pain as a colour. What would it be? Try using that colour and draw a shape that feels like the shape of your pain. You can keep on using colours and shapes to add all the different bits of pain you may feel. Or you might want to draw things or people associated with your pain.

The ways you express feelings need to fit in with your personality, things you like to do and feel comfortable with.

MANY WAYS OF EXPRESSING FEELINGS

If you like writing, you could write a journal, poetry or letter about how you feel. Or you could write words and phrases about your feelings in big letters and stick it on your wall.

You could sometimes choose what you wear to express how you are feeling; e.g. you could honour your grief by wearing the colours of mourning - black, purple, etc.

You could do things at home or in your garden which express important things for you, like planting something in remembrance of your sadness, or putting up pictures or photos which seem to 'speak' for your feelings.

Explore music that seems to express some of your feelings. Blues; soul; piano, violin or guitar music; songs; water, whale and dolphin sounds - it's what suits you that matters.

Talking to someone else who cares is very important. We need others to know how we feel, how bad things are. If you can't tell anyone you know, ring a helpline. Try not to be alone with your pain and despair any longer.

SOOTHING THE PAIN

When we feel emotional pain, we usually experience it somewhere inside our bodies. Some of the places people mention when they talk about the hurts inside them include their heart, their chest, their tummy and their throat. It's a very individual thing. Ways people describe feeling inside include aching, sore, cold, wounded, broken... It can be many things. However you experience your pain in your body, it can help to try to soothe the hurt.

THE PLACES THAT HURT

Try to identify where inside of you feels hurt or wounded. This just means sitting and paying attention to your body, and how it feels. Don't forget to breathe.

Ask yourself where inside you feels hurt in any way. Don't push yourself too much. Just taking a moment to notice one place inside where you hurt is a good start. Perhaps lay your hand on it. If you like, you could draw the outline of your body on a piece of paper and show where it hurts.

The 'wounds' or hurts inside you need soothing and helping to heal up. There are lots of ways you can do this, like:

Holding a pillow, cushion, hot water bottle or other 'comforter' against the place where you feel hurt. Or wrap a scarf or blanket (like a big bandage) round you.

Having a cry for the hurt parts of you and then saying gentle, comforting things to yourself, like "it's okay now..."

A soothing drink, like warm milk, hot chocolate, tea or herb tea, water with Rescue Remedy in (whatever is comforting).

GETTING A BREAK FROM FEELINGS

Sometimes you don't want to think about what's going on inside you. You just want to escape from all the thinking and feeling. Self-harm might be your way of doing this, taking you away from all the awful feelings.

DISTRACTING YOURSELF

You could try distracting yourself in other ways. One way could be to let something else express the feelings for you, such as loud music. Imagine the person singing has the feelings and is screaming them out.

Or you could imagine parcelling up the feelings and putting them somewhere safe until you are ready to face them.

When I just couldn't face any more pain I would imagine taking a black dustbin bag and, one by one, place all the horrible feelings in it. When it was full I would imagine tying up the top and sending it off through space.

Sometimes I would send it off as far as I could but other times I would send it somewhere specific, like to the room where my group used to meet. I knew it would be safe there and I could open it later with people around me who would understand and help me deal with it all. (L.C.)

THINGS TO DO WHEN FEELINGS ARE TOO MUCH

You could work out for yourself a list of things you can do when you need to get away from unbearable feelings for a while. Big or small things; things which suit you. The sorts of things which could help include:

Physical things like walking, running, swimming, cycling, going to the gym (or get yourself some cheap weights and something like a bouncy 'jogger' to use at home).

Things that occupy your mind, like reading, TV, playing computer games, or games like chess or 'patience', doing some work or study, sewing, drawing, woodwork.

Some people find doing something domestic is good, like cleaning, baking, home decorating or gardening.

Things that bring you into contact with other people, or perhaps animals (walking someone's dog?).

THINGS TO REMIND YOURSELF OF

The things which have hurt me in my life are real and important, even if they don't show.

My feelings are valid and justified. They deserve to be recognised.

Sometimes I may need a break from the pain; to postpone my feelings until I have someone to help me with them.

If I let myself really have my feelings and get support for them, they will pass. The pain won't go on for ever.

NEEDING TO TAKE SOME CONTROL

You may have experienced very little control over your life and the things that have happened to you. Other people may have had a lot of control over you. This can lead to feelings of utter helplessness. Self-harm may be the only thing in your life that gives you a sense of control. You may be harming your body, but at least it's your decision to harm it and not someone else's.

TAKING CONTROL IN SMALL WAYS

Taking control over other things in your life can lessen that awful feeling of helplessness. You could start with small things, like deciding when and what you will eat. Just for a change think about what *you* would like.

You could also think about other small, everyday things you can have more choice and control in, like:

going to bed, getting up, having a bath etc. when *you* want

wearing what you fancy, not what others expect; looking how *you* feel like looking

choosing TV programmes, books, music etc. *you* like

taking time away for yourself for your own private thoughts

"Once I decided to have ice cream for breakfast. It seemed a very daring thing to do. My mother would have had a fit! I really enjoyed it and for the rest of the day I felt a mixture of excitement and being in charge of myself. It was great."

When you are feeling that you have no control over your life, or some aspects of it, all sorts of other feelings arise. You can feel powerless, angry, despairing, frustrated, 'crazy', depressed, diminished or humiliated - different things at different times. Perhaps you turn these feelings in on yourself. Finding a way of protesting about your lack of control (now or in the past) can help you feel more powerful and less overwhelmed by awful feelings.

MAKING YOUR PROTEST

You may feel able to protest directly to people who have had control over you, and that could help you take back some power and feel better. But this may not be possible. Throughout history, people who have had their power taken away from them - like prisoners of war - have survived by recording their protest in some way, if only for themselves. One way has been to write graffiti on their prison walls.

You could have your own graffiti 'wall', using a roll of paper, and write words or statements or draw pictures or cartoons expressing your protest. You can show your anger and pain, or make fun of those who have had power over you. You could show yourself as strong and powerful.

If you like, you could also do other things like write poetry or songs of protest about your experience.

THINGS TO REMIND YOURSELF OF

I have the right to control in my own life.

I can take back control in small ways (and big!).

I have the right to be angry and to protest.

The yellow file

Not another one!
Go away and give me a break,
You posh, clean, protected person.
Who are you anyway?

You don't even let me smoke,
Yet you cut me up inside and take out my heart
And I desperately allow you to,
Hoping you will save me.

Well, go to your next guinea pig
And leave me alone.
I'll go to the tramp under the bridge,
He'll offer me a butt end, not a yellow file.

Don't mess around with me any more.
I ain't buying your hypocrisy no more.
And by the way!! Just for the record -
I don't see no file with your name in it!!!

Karen

31

EXPLODING WITH ANGER

Anger is a valid and important emotion, yet it can be very difficult for us to express, or even admit to.

Some people feel so ashamed and afraid of their own anger, that they dare not even let themselves *feel* angry, let alone show anger. It can feel like being angry makes you 'bad'. In this painful situation all the person's anger may be turned inwards on themselves. They may get depressed and despairing, and self-harm in a surge of self-hatred.

It's not surprising that we often fear anger, if we have experienced other people expressing their anger abusively or hurtfully. Yet anger doesn't have to be destructive. Anger can be very important, as it is what can help us to stand up for ourselves and others.

EXPLORING YOUR ANGER

IF I WAS ANGRY...

In your own head, out loud to yourself, or on paper, ask yourself the question:

"if I was angry, what would it be about?"

then just say (or write) anything that comes into your head. If you feel scared of the word 'angry' say 'annoyed' or 'cross'. You might think of particular people you are cross with, or things that have happened, or you might feel you're angry with everything and everybody.

Sometimes people fear their anger because it feels so enormous. It feels like it would overwhelm them. They may fear they'd hurt someone else if they didn't self-harm. The next exercise is good, if you feel like that.

HOW BIG IS MY ANGER?

This time say to yourself:

"if I really got angry, I'd"....

and say aloud or write down the answers, like 'I'd explode', 'I'd kill someone', 'I'd smash the world up', etc. (you may also find you have fears like 'everyone would hate me').

You could also draw your anger on paper, showing it in whatever colours seem right - red, black, purple? Use whatever shapes or symbols convey its power, such as jagged or explosive images, whatever feels right.

EXPRESSING YOUR ANGER

Whether or not we would really hurt anyone with our anger, we all need to find ways of expressing angry feelings safely and satisfactorily. Sometimes we need to communicate our anger directly - to tell someone in our lives now "I'm angry" about something they have done. Sometimes that is not possible because the person is no longer around, or it would be risky to do so, or we just don't want to. Even then, it's good to express for our own benefit the things we'd like to say to that person, if we could.

Writing letters (or talking a letter onto a tape) is a really good way of sorting out and expressing angry feelings towards people, whether or not you actually send the letter.

WRITING AN ANGRY LETTER

Write or dictate a letter saying all your angry feelings to the person or people concerned. Don't hold back - be as furious as you want, even if it seems unreasonable. No-one has to see or hear this. If you want, you can write about what nasty things you'd like to do to the person, or wish would happen to them.

Later on you can decide whether you want to actually say or send any of what you have said in the letter to the people involved. You might want to write another, more measured letter which you do send. (Be a bit careful what you write down to send - if you put threats in a letter the person could take it to the police.) Or you might just want to keep the letter somewhere private, or stick it up on your wall and enjoy looking at it!

Sometimes you can't do anything directly about the hurts and injustices you have suffered. But your anger is still important and needs to be expressed. Otherwise it sits inside you, making you tense, miserable and self-hating.

People can feel like they don't want to let go of their anger, unless they can show it directly to those they are angry with. Self-harm can feel like the only way to do justice to their outrage. If you feel like this, you are right not to want your anger trivialised. But why should you be hurt further? It's better to find other powerful ways of expressing your anger. In this way you acknowledge and honour your feelings, and do justice to yourself.

MANY WAYS OF EXPRESSING ANGER

Drawing: perhaps a picture of the person you are angry with, showing on it what you want to do to them, scribbling on the picture, tearing it, jumping on it, even spitting at it!

Writing - a few words, big, in thick marker pen - like a shout on the paper. Or you could write about the experiences you are angry about, perhaps for a newsletter.

Throwing things or hitting something. Throwing cutlery on the floor makes a satisfying noise. Hurling bottles into the bottle bank is good too. A dartboard is great, (you can imagine aiming darts at people you are angry with). You can whack the bed with a tennis racket, or use a big cushion (or home-made punchbag) to punch or kick. (Don't hurt yourself, or smash things which are precious to you.)

Some sorts of physical exercise are really helpful, like table tennis or squash, football, self-defence... Fast digging or hoovering could also help you let off steam. So can tearing up newspapers or phone books.

Making figures and objects out of plasticine, play-dough or clay which represent something you are angry about, and then doing something appropriate with them - like smashing them, burying them, flattening them... Clay (or mud) is also great to throw at a wall - perhaps out in the garden!

Directing my anger where it belongs, making me feel big
and powerful and my abuser seem small and helpless.
J.

THINGS TO REMIND YOURSELF OF

Anger is natural and healthy. I'm not bad for being angry.

I have a right to protest about being treated badly.

I can let out my anger for my own relief and satisfaction.

FEELING GUILT AND SHAME

Many people who harm themselves do so at least partly in order to punish themselves, and try to rid themselves of feelings of guilt, shame, 'badness' and 'dirtiness'. Often they have done nothing to deserve to feel so bad.

We all do things at times in our lives about which we feel justly ashamed or remorseful. Then we need to think about whether there is any way we can put right the situation - perhaps by apologising and allowing the person we have hurt to tell us how they feel. However, most of the time people who self-harm feel shame and guilt *unjustly*, because of things which have been done *to* them.

It is terrible to carry around the burden of guilt or shame. Guilt can make you so miserable that it's impossible to enjoy anything, as though there were permanently dark clouds across the sun. Shame can make you feel so bad that it seems unbearable to *be* yourself. At the same time it can make you afraid to be with others, in case they see how 'awful', 'dirty' or 'ugly' you are (or so you believe).

What can you do about such feelings? The first thing is to realise that *feeling* bad or dirty does not mean you actually *are* those things. If you feel guilty or ashamed, this is how you have been *made to feel* by things in your life.

Imagine a beautiful new baby, or a young child. You were once like that. To a child, the adults around act like mirrors. If they love and are delighted by their baby, the baby comes to feel himself to be loveable and delightful. If they are interested in and proud of their child, the child feels herself to be interesting and worthwhile.

If, on the other hand, the adults around a child ridicule and criticise her, the child feels bad, useless and ridiculous. If they treat her abusively, as though she is just something to use or vent their anger and self-hatred on, the child comes to feel worthless and hateful.

WHERE GUILT AND SHAME COME FROM

Think of the things (big or small) which have happened in your life which have left you feeling bad, ashamed, dirty, wrong, etc. Recall any situations now in your life which tend to leave you feeling horrible about yourself. Write them in a list on paper or say them on to tape.

Looking at the list, can you see how your guilt and shame are feelings which have been caused by what has happened to you? It is not **your** shame or guilt you feel, these feelings have been dumped upon you. It's time to dump them back where they came from.

If you are someone who tends to suffer horrible feelings of self-hatred, guilt and shame, you will know how hard it is to change them. They can't easily be just argued away. In fact, feelings of shame and guilt need to be explored and expressed. Easing them is a gradual process, which starts with just becoming more aware of the feelings and of the pain they cause you. It's very helpful if you can talk about the feelings with someone who will understand and care and support you. It's also good to write about what you feel, as well as to express it through drawing.

Shame

The shame I bear
because you touched me for your pleasure
I carry the blame
The word 'abused' branded across my forehead
Which has melted into my identity
Stealing my sexuality.

Because you could not control your lust I suffer
My face on the floor with embarrassment
Hair across my eyes
THE SHAME I HAVE BECAUSE YOU ABUSED ME.
My head bowed low in disgrace
Because of a childhood dishonoured.
Rebecca

Dark prison of my guilt and self-hatred **L**

DEPICTING SHAME AND GUILT

Draw a simple picture of yourself (a stick or blob figure will do fine). On the same piece of paper, try to show your shame, guilt, 'badness', 'dirtiness', or whatever. Draw it in a way which shows how it makes you feel. Show it in whatever way seems right - say as a big weight on top of you, as a smear or blotch, as a 'hook' on which you hang... Then look at the picture. How does it make you feel? Seeing the awfulness and injustice of the shame or guilt there, you may feel sad or angry.

The next stage is to *change* the picture. (If you feel you want to keep this picture as it is, then take some more paper and do a new picture on that.) Now draw what you would like to happen to the shame and guilt. Would you like to destroy them, rub them out, or give them to someone else? Show yourself how you would like things to be - free of the burden of horrible feelings that have been forced upon you. Show yourself as you are - beautiful and good.

Sometimes it's very hard to feel better about ourselves. The bad, self-hating feelings are so strong, they can just drown out any attempts to tell ourselves that they are not justified. One helpful thing to do can be to give voice to the hateful feelings and thoughts, rather than to just have them raging inside and driving you to self-harm. Then you can really look at what you are saying to yourself and decide what you think about it. Having voiced these negative thoughts, sometimes you can find a kinder, more positive voice inside yourself.

Negative Voices

As far back as I can remember I have always had negative voices in my head - forever telling me that I was stupid, a fat bitch, a pathetic idiot, etc. Somewhere very, very deep inside me, on rare occasions, I did feel that I wasn't these things. My head said I was. But in fact deep inside I believed I was beautiful inside __and__ outside. But the negative voices were always the most powerful - they always won.

On many occasions I would be criticising myself so much that I would often impulsively punch myself in the face or plan to hurt myself in some way when I was alone. I desperately felt I had to punish myself for being so stupid and pathetic!

41

Once this had been achieved I felt better knowing that I had __yet again__ punished myself for being me.

That was all in the past.

Today my life is changing so much, I do still have lots of negative messages in my head but the miracle is, I'm now opening my ears more and hearing that beautiful little me deep inside. I have conversations with my little voice inside, we have become friends. I am in touch with her at long last. She tells me I am okay, she tells me it wasn't my fault, she encourages me to hold my head up high to the sun, she tells me my body is mine and that my body is beautiful. She is becoming the friend I have always wanted.

I do feel so sad, that she was there all the time but the negative voices kept us so far apart. But we are together now and we are getting stronger and stronger each day. I really feel that what's helped me learn to forgive myself and accept myself is the unconditional kindness and respect I have received from the people I know in my life today. I decided that I no longer would have people in my life who shame me or don't accept me for who I am.
Karen

THINGS TO REMIND YOURSELF OF

I am not bad, dirty, or horrible. I have been made to feel like that by things that have happened. But it's not true.

I don't have to keep believing horrible things about myself. I can chuck them out, and start seeing the good in me.

Sometimes I hate myself instead of hating someone else. I can turn my anger back onto those who deserve it.

FEELING EMPTY AND NEEDY

Sometimes self-harm is about trying to deal with desperate feelings of emptiness, neediness and lack of comfort. For some people it can be very comforting when they look after an injury they have made, or when someone else treats it for them. It's as though, in a way, the bathing and bandaging help soothe and treat not just that injury, but the wounds and pain they feel *inside*. Other people sometimes swallow tablets or other things to try to quieten and ease the terrible emotional pain they feel inside themselves.

If you are someone who does this, then you are already trying to do something really important: to soothe the hurts that your life has caused you. It's sad that your efforts to do this good thing for yourself cause you more pain, hurt and danger. What you can try to do is to find ways of soothing the inner wounds you carry, without having to harm yourself.

It might be easy to say "take care of yourself", but often it is not so easy to do. Several things can happen when you think about comforting yourself. You may want to, but not know how. You might be angry, feeling "No-one has ever cared about me or comforted me, why should I have to do it for myself?". You're right to feel angry and resentful if you haven't had the loving and caring you have needed. And you do still need support and comfort from others, but it does help to give some to yourself too.

You might think that it's 'stupid' to need comfort, let alone to give it to yourself. Perhaps the whole thing sounds like a load of rubbish. Sometimes saying something is 'stupid' is less painful. But if you are someone who self-harms, you probably do need some comfort and caring. You could give the ideas that follow a try anyway.

WORDS OF COMFORT

One good thing you can do if you feel empty or needy and desperate for comfort is to ask yourself: *"what would I like someone to say to me right now?"*

The 'someone' needs to be somebody caring and loving. It could be a real person you know, or you could visualise in your imagination a person who you would like to really care for you. Then you think about what lovely, comforting, caring things you'd like them to say to you. You could write them down. This would be very individual, but could be something like *"I know you're in awful pain"*, *"You're not on your own, I'll help you"*, *"It's all right, I'll look after you"* - anything which would feel comforting and helpful to you.

What you do next is to say those same comforting things to yourself. Sometimes you can be the comforting figure you need, for the part of yourself which is deprived and needy. You can say those gentle, loving things to yourself. You could also think if there's someone in your life who would give you a bit of the same sort of comfort - now or later.

If you feel like harming yourself, it's often a signal that there is something you need. Part of you (usually a part that doesn't get heard enough!) is desperately trying to communicate that need. Often the part that is so needy and desperate feels very young. It can be hard to know exactly what it is that you actually need.

44

SOMETHING I NEED

Start with the assumption that there is something which you need, and that this is important. Take a few minutes to explore possibilities and listen to yourself. Either write down or say (out loud or to yourself): *"I need ..."*

Take notice of what thoughts follow. Write or say as many things as you can, big or small. It's fine if they're contradictory. If you find yourself too uptight about getting it right, change the statement to *"maybe I need"*. Or it might be easier to say *"she needs"* or *"he needs"*, about yourself.

Once you've got some ideas about things you might need, you can think about ways of getting them. Try to take seriously what you have said about what you need. You've had more than enough of being dismissed and ignored. See what things on your list are possible, and what you could give yourself or ask for from others.

> *Strong, safe arms to enfold me*
> *Soft, kind voice to comfort me*
> *Open mind to believe me*
> *Warm heart to accept me*
> *Strength to have faith in me*
> *Patience to wait for me.*
>
> *Pip*

Things that have helped me

Touching my cat's
velvet paw, music, sunshine,
spiders' webs, acorns, conkers, leaves,
saving frogs, ants, wind, rain,
cutting, loving, being heard, loved, cared for,
appreciated, respected. Equality. I also enjoy
swimming like a dolphin in the sea, being with safe people,
good friends, my school teacher.
Tea, coffee, ginger biscuits,
rum truffles, looking at the stars, lighting a candle,
having a hot bath at night, watching 'Prisoner Cell Block H'.
Getting back into bed. Having a good sesh with
friends, reading 'Andy Capp' and 'The Beano'.
Writing poems. Keeping my power, and getting a good
bargain from the charity shop. Curly Wurlies,
wine gums, and peace of mind
would be nice also.
Karen

THINGS TO REMIND YOURSELF OF

It's okay to feel needy. Everyone does sometimes (even if they don't admit it). I don't deserve to be punished for it.

It can be very painful to let yourself feel your needs. I can take it slowly and be kind to myself.

I can have some comfort. I can take care of myself and ask others for some of what I need.

IT'S WHO YOU ARE

Self-harm can feel so much part of you that you cannot imagine who you would be without it. This may be because you have grown up with very little sense of who you are and maybe haven't had much chance to discover who you might be. It can be very hard to think about who you are. Sometimes it can feel like there is nothing there - that you don't exist. Self-harm can fill that emptiness, can make you feel 'this is who I am'.

FINDING OUT ABOUT ME

Trying to find out who you are or might be can feel very scary. But you don't have to do it all at once. You could start by making a list of things that you like. It could be colours you like, particular foods or flowers, or even the time of year you like best. Anything at all that you like or prefer. When you have written some things you could read it to yourself saying, 'I like .... and I like .... I am a person who likes .... "

This is only a small part of who you are but it's a start. Another time you could make a list of things you can do. These could include skills such as driving, cooking, DIY, sewing, decorating, or anything else, no matter how small.

When you are feeling like going a bit further you could list all the good qualities you have, like being a good listener, having a sense of humour, or anything else you value in other people.

Although finding out who you are can be a frightening idea it can also be the beginning of an adventure. Just imagine meeting a good friend who you haven't seen for years - maybe not since childhood. You would have so much you wanted to know about her. Even though the things you find out wouldn't change her they would help you to feel closer to her. It's just like that discovering yourself. There's a whole, wonderful person there waiting to be found.

A Chance

I need a chance, to be just me,
To show what I can really be.
I need a chance, to be just me,
Maybe so you can see
Not half, but all of me.
I need a chance, can't you see
That I want to be just me!

Shaz.

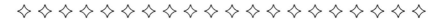

Often we hide and deny some parts or aspects of ourselves. Sometimes self-harm expresses (in a 'coded' way) parts of ourselves we think are unacceptable or shameful. For example, if someone has grown up being taught that they must always be 'nice' and sweet and quiet, injuring themselves may be a way they express the part of themselves that doesn't feel 'nice', that wants to be loud and rebellious. Or if someone has been made to feel that they must always be 'strong' and uncomplaining, the wounds they cause themselves may be a way of showing that they are vulnerable and can be hurt.

MAKING MY MARK

When people write graffiti on walls it often stems from a
need to make their mark and express something of
themselves. Graffiti can be anything - words, pictures,
poems, slogans...   Cover part of your wall with paper.
Then do graffiti on it to say anything you want about
yourself and what you think and believe in. It could be
about you, or important things you'd like to say to the world.
You can keep adding more graffiti over time as you think of
new things you want to say.

You could also draw an outline of your body on a big sheet
of paper, and write 'messages' on that - things about
yourself which maybe you don't usually show. You could
add other things to the picture - facial expressions, hair,
wings, things which express something important for you.

People in some countries do elaborate paintings on their
bodies, which express powerful things. You could use face
paints to write or draw your 'messages' on your own skin.

THINGS TO REMIND YOURSELF OF

I don't have to invent a self - it's already there just waiting
to be discovered.

I can take my time about discovering myself, starting with
really small things.

There are many aspects to me, and they are all valid parts
of the whole me. It's okay to be me.

FEELING UNREAL OR PANICKY

Sometimes people self-harm as a way of helping themselves feel more 'real' at a time when they are feeling 'unreal', 'numb' or 'distant'. People may also use hurting themselves to help them to come back down to earth when they are feeling panicky or frantic with anxiety.

Feeling unreal or very panicky can be frightening, horrible and confusing. It can make you feel as though you are going mad, as though something terrible is going to happen, as though you are going to die.

It can seem like the feelings have just come from nowhere, and taken you over. In fact, numbness and panic are both responses to overwhelming experiences and feelings, which may have begun long in the past. The trouble is, that for some people the unrealness and panic keep coming back later, when the original trauma or distress is over. But people can find ways to take control of these feelings.

Often, feelings of unrealness or panic come back when someone is anxious or under some stress. This might be because of something which would generally be acknowledged as stressful, such as pressure at work, exams, moving house, bereavement, having an accident, and so on. Or it might be because of some situation which is stressful to the individual concerned (however apparently small or easy to others), perhaps because of their past experiences. Most people are also more vulnerable to feeling unreal or getting panicky when they are tired or hungry.

WHAT MAKES ME FEEL PANICKY OR UNREAL?

One helpful thing to do is to become more familiar with what happens to you, when and why. Some ways to do this are:

Keep a diary of feelings and things that happen. Try to write something brief several times a day. Over time this will help you to see patterns: - when the unreal or panicky feelings seem to start, and what seems to set them off.

When you start to feel unreal or panicky (or afterwards), think about the particular situation you are (or were) in at that moment, and about your life generally. Is there anything, however apparently small, which feels stressful, worrying, upsetting or too much for you?

Ask yourself the question: "What would I be feeling if I wasn't feeling unreal / panicky?" The answer might give you clues about feelings which are hard for you to bear (such as sadness or anger). You may be protecting yourself from these feelings by going numb or panicky. Or it might tell you that you are hungry, or tired, or fed-up....

When you understand more about the circumstances and feelings which trigger feelings of unreality or panic for you, you can think about things you could change in your life to reduce the stress on you. Or you might need to get more support for feelings which are hard for you to bear.

There are also ways to stop feeling unreal or panicky, when it happens.

DEALING WITH FEELINGS OF UNREALITY OR PANIC

1. Don't make the situation any worse by worrying or feeling bad about it. Don't pretend it's not happening. Just notice and accept what's going on. You could say something to yourself like "Oh, I'm getting those feelings again. It's okay, I'm alright. It will pass".

2. Make sure you are breathing properly. Holding or restricting your breath, or breathing too fast can make you panic and feel very unreal. Try to let yourself breathe slowly and easily, really letting your breath **out**. You could put your hand on your tummy and feel yourself breathing.

3. You might be scrunching yourself up in your body, which stops the blood flowing easily and can make you feel unreal or anxious. Get yourself comfortable, sitting or standing up with your body supported. Relax your body.

4. Feel your body and what it is touching. Make sure your feet are touching the ground, perhaps rub them on the floor a bit to really feel them. Feel your hands, rubbing your fingers together. Run your hands over your body or face and see how that feels. You could put your hand on your heart and feel your heartbeat. You could hug yourself too.

5. When you feel like it, have a look around you at the place you are in and things nearby. Focus on one or two things around, and notice what they really look like. Don't worry about the world beyond that. If you can, touch the things and feel your skin in contact with them. Listen to the sounds you can hear around you.

Another good thing to do for yourself is to have a list of things which help you feel more calm or real. Here is a list of things other people find helpful. You might find other things that work for you, too.

QUICK WAYS OF FEELING CALMER AND MORE REAL

Having a drink of water or juice; putting some ice cubes in it to crunch can be good. Herb teas can help.

Doing something physical but calm, like walking (be sure you go somewhere you feel safe).

If you are feeling numb' or 'out of it', cold water can help - splashing yourself, or if you feel safe enough, swimming.

Putting yourself to bed or wrapped up on the sofa.

Listening to calm music, letting yourself focus and relax.

Looking at photos or things which are precious to you.

Telling someone you trust what you are feeling. Holding their hand if you want to.

THINGS TO REMIND YOURSELF OF

It's horrible to feel panicky or unreal, but nothing terrible is going to happen.

The feelings will pass if I take care of myself.

It's okay to want help from someone else, too.

SENDING A MESSAGE

Sometimes people self-harm to try to send a message to someone else. They may be trying to communicate their feelings, or to get something they need. Or they may be expressing their distress about some way the other person behaves. With self-harm, the communication is indirect, and the hope is that the 'message' will be received and understood. Unfortunately, the message may be unclear, or may be misunderstood or not heard.

We all need to find ways to communicate important things to other people, and this can be very hard. Sometimes others don't want to hear. But we need to give ourselves and other people a chance to get things across.

GETTING THE MESSAGE

The first thing to do is be clear for yourself what 'message' you need to send, and who to. Get a sheet of paper and cut it into strips. Write on each strip some sort of short message. You don't have to get it right straight away, try out lots of different things you could be needing to say. Then look through the strips. From amongst them, which ones seem to be the messages you need to send at this particular time? Who would you want to receive them? Would it be a particular person, or the world at large?

The next step is to think about how you could communicate your message. You could say it in words. You could show them the slips of paper, or write them out big and stick on the wall. Maybe you need to write something longer in a letter, or send a card.

Sometimes it isn't possible for you to communicate your message directly to the person it is aimed at. At those times, you could show it to someone else instead, and explain how you would like to say these things to the person concerned. Someone supportive, like a friend or a counsellor would understand.

You might also need to express your anger and frustration about not being able to give your messages to the person who needs to hear them.

✧ ✧

BASTARD

I HURT

LEAVE ME ALONE

YOU DON'T CARE

HELP

✧ ✧

BUILDING YOUR STRENGTHS

RECLAIMING YOUR BODY

Self-harm is about something you do to your body. Many people who self-harm have very difficult and unhappy feelings about their own bodies. This is usually because things have happened to them which have *made* them feel bad or uncomfortable about their bodies.

Some people hate their body, telling themselves horrible things about it, or about particular parts of it. Sometimes their body has come to feel like an 'enemy'. They hate it for being vulnerable, for having needs, for being hurt.

With self-harm, sometimes it seems like people are trying to 'punish' or reject their own body. Perhaps it feels like their body is to blame for bad things that have happened. Of course, it's never the person's own fault if others have hurt them. No-one's body deserves to be abused or exploited. But it's not surprising that people who have been treated badly find it hard to love their own bodies. How can you possibly feel good about your body (or yourself) if you have been treated as though you and your body don't matter, and have no rights or feelings?

People in this painful situation have the task of trying to 'forgive' their bodies for the crimes which others have done to them. From such difficult beginnings, they need to create some good feelings about their bodies. If you hate your body, you can learn to feel better about it, to begin to see it as tender and precious, rather than as a horrible thing to be punished. It's hard. But it can be done.

THINGS I LIKE ABOUT MY BODY

Even when you hate your body it can be possible to find some things you like, or some things your body is capable of that please you. It can be good to make a picture of these things, but instead of drawing it you could look through old magazines to find images you can relate to.

You may find images relating to strength or softness. If you are big you may find positive images of people or things that are big. Or if you are small you could look for positive images of smallness. If you like a particular part of your body look for good pictures that represent that part, or what that part does. It might seem hard but once you start looking at images you will find you connect with some of them. You might even find yourself connecting with some surprising images.

When you are satisfied with your selection you can paste them on to a large sheet of paper. You can have fun arranging them. You could put the picture on a wall and each time you look at it you can remind yourself that there are things you do like about your body.

Some people feel like their body doesn't really belong to them. Maybe it feels like other people have taken over or 'stolen' their body from them. Sometimes people can feel like they don't want much to do with their own bodies. Perhaps it just feels too painful to even *have* a body. People also cut off from physical feelings, to stop themselves feeling unbearable emotional pain. They might feel numb or very separate from their own body.

Someone may also self-harm to claim back their body, to say "this is mine, this is me". Or if their body feels numb or strange to them, they might hurt it to try to feel *something,* to find some way of relating to it. If self-harm has these powerful meanings for you, it can help to find some other ways of reclaiming your body.

CLAIMING BACK YOUR BODY

You could try out some ways of connecting with your body and claiming it for yourself. There's bound to be something that suits you. Take it slowly and only do what feels safe and comfortable. Here are some things other people who have struggled with this issue have found helpful:

Starting to try to pay more attention to your body and how it feels at different times. Noticing things like feeling cold or uncomfortable or hungry or tired and responding to them.

Getting to know how your body looks, from the mirror and photos - old and recent. Don't compare yourself with pictures of supermodels (if you want to see what 'real people' look like, go to the swimming pool or beach!). You can get to know how your body feels, too, with your hands.

Physical activities like walking, swimming, dancing, rock-climbing, running, yoga, learning self-defence, etc.

Doing nice things for your body, like putting on body lotion, stroking yourself, relaxing by the fire, a jacuzzi!..

Getting other people to do nice things for your body, like rubbing your feet, a shiatsu massage, aromatherapy, healing. Only do this when you feel safe and ready.

FEELING GOOD ABOUT YOURSELF

It's hard to feel good about yourself when you have been treated badly. You grow up with messages in your head about how useless, stupid, no good and awful you are. When things like this have been said to you, or you have been treated as if you are these things, then you begin to believe them. Even when no-one else is saying them you can find yourself saying them.

It is important to build up new messages to yourself about how worthwhile and important you are. It will be difficult at first and you may not believe them but if you persevere you can change how you feel in the end.

GOOD THINGS ABOUT ME

You could write a list of all the good things about you. You could start with how resourceful you are to have discovered self-harm as a way of surviving. Even if you don't want to go on using this method it was amazing that you found it when you did. You could think about all the things that are difficult for you at the moment and at the end of every day write a list of what you have achieved. This might include things like getting out of bed and facing the day (or deciding that the best thing for you was to stay in bed), good things you have managed to say to yourself like 'I'm a nice person', or anything else no matter how small.

Doing something nice for yourself can help you feel worthwhile. It's easy to get into a vicious circle where you won't do anything nice for yourself because you feel you don't deserve it and end up feeling even worse about yourself. Yet doing things for yourself can help you to like yourself more. You could try breaking through this circle by taking yourself to a different place - this can be a real place, or it can be changing your mood.

LIFTING THE SPIRIT

You could go to a lovely place. If you live in the countryside or by the sea this won't be too difficult. If you live in a city then perhaps a park or by a river.

Try to notice everything around you - the different colours and shapes of things growing, the smells and sounds. Look at the sky and notice the shapes of the clouds and how they move. Try to think of nothing else but these things - let them become part of you. Breathe them in. Allow yourself to take in all the good feelings of your surroundings and you will feel your spirit lift.

Creating good feelings can help you to like yourself. You can also do this indoors by playing some beautiful music.

LISTENING TO MUSIC

First make sure you are comfortable. Are you warm enough? Do you need a blanket? Do you want to lie down or would you prefer a comfortable chair?

Choose some music you really like. Let yourself enter into the music and feel it enter you. Imagine you are the music, floating, flying - however it takes you. Leave everything else behind. When the music finishes you could play it again if you like. When you have finished listening try to keep hold of the good feelings it evoked in you. Cuddle up to yourself, holding the feelings inside you.

How do I look after myself?

One of the biggest changes that's happened in my life is to stop running. Run, run, run, that's all I seem to have done in my life. Then suddenly I couldn't do it anymore. I was completely exhausted and I just could not find the physical and emotional energy to carry on. For a long time I betrayed myself for this - messages 'get out there, enjoy life, pick yourself up, dust yourself down' etc., hammered in my head - but only seemed to cause me mental anguish and reinforced the stuckness I felt.

In stopping running, gradually I've been able to stop and look back over my life and accept the knowledge I was abused by my father, and that's painful. And yet in stopping chasing love, I've found I'm beginning to enjoy me/my life on a much deeper level.

I have started getting loads of pleasure from nature, particularly birds at the moment. When I was small and I got scared my family would say the birds would look after me - and somehow, despite the abuse, that has definitely survived. By hearing birds sing I know I am in touch with nature - and something bigger than me, life giving. I've started feeding them daily and somehow it makes me feed myself daily too, which I've always found difficult. It's like if I can feed the birds I have compassion and love enough to feed myself.

I've also begun identifying birds and their songs - previously something I relied upon others to do for me. It's like coming home, owning my own vulnerabilities and pleasures.

Robyn Dylan-Eil Don

61

How you feel about yourself can be reflected in your environment. But it works the other way round too. Making your environment beautiful can help you to feel beautiful and deserving. It can be hard to allow yourself to have nice things but you deserve them. If you haven't much money it can seem not worth trying but there is lots you can do that won't cost much. You can collect beautiful things from nature and display them in your home, like fir cones, shells, pretty stones, etc. You can decorate your walls with things you write or draw.

✧ ✧

My peaceful place **Pip**

✧ ✧

THINGS TO REMIND YOURSELF OF

I am worth caring about and doing nice things for

I am a worthwhile person with lots to offer

I matter and my life matters

RELATIONSHIPS WITH OTHER PEOPLE

As you begin to care for yourself more you may become more aware of how other people treat you. You may become dissatisfied with things you accepted in the past. If other people don't treat you well it can undermine all the good feelings you have been building up.

It can be very scary to question relationships you depend on, but you can take this slowly. You may find that some people don't want you to change. It may be that they find change unsettling, or that they are getting something out of you staying the same. They may feel that if you don't need them in the same way then you won't want them in your life.

It is important for you to find out what you want from others, and what you like and don't like about your relationships.

WHAT I WANT FROM OTHER PEOPLE

Take a piece of paper and draw a line down the middle. On one side list "What I would like to get from friends". (This includes how you want to be treated.) On the other side list: "What I get from friends". When you have finished compare the two lists. Ask yourself "Am I getting what I want from my friends?" "What is missing?" "What isn't okay?" "What would I like to change?"

You can do this about friendships or other relationships generally, or about a particular relationship.

When you feel clearer about what you want and don't want from people the next step may be to tell them. This can feel terrifying. But remember you don't have to do it all at once. Choose one thing you want to change or ask for, and try saying something. Try saying it out loud to yourself first. It may be something like "When you do/say .... I feel put down. Could you try not to do/say that." Or something you need, like "I've had an awful day, can I tell you about it?".

Sometimes we don't feel able to tell someone directly about something we feel unhappy about in a relationship. Or we might try, but it doesn't seem to make any difference. What you can do then is to try to change the way *you* are with the other person. You could see a relationship like a dance, where each person does particular steps. If you change some of your 'steps', the 'dance' (or relationship) will change. Say, for example, you feel that you do all the listening, giving and supporting in a relationship. You could decide to stop being quite so available and sympathetic all the time, and to make deliberate attempts to talk about your life more.

You may feel that some relationships are beyond salvation! They are too destructive to you, and the other people are not open to change. If so, then you may need to end the relationship. It can be hard to let go of unsatisfactory relationships, if you haven't got many friends or people you feel close to. So take your time. As you change and your self-esteem grows, you will find yourself making new sorts of friends.

Where you are unsafe in a relationship, the need to get away may be more urgent. You might need to get some support to help you break away from people who are harmful to you.

GETTING SUPPORT

Support is something which everybody in the world needs. By 'support' we mean having contact with people who care about you, who take you seriously, who will help you at hard times. We need different people, to give us different sorts of things. Support can also mean things other than people, like a decent place to live, things you do to relax, animals, - things which 'feed' you and help you to feel okay. Here we are mainly talking about the sorts of support we get from other people. All human beings need this, although they may not all recognise or admit it!

As children we needed to be supported, and not to have to support the adults around us. As well as being taken care of physically, we needed to be helped to understand, express and manage our feelings and needs, to make relationships, to explore and express ourselves.

If things go okay when we are children, then as we grow up we are able to give support to others, as well as to receive it. We become interdependent, or mutually supportive with others. But if we didn't get the support we needed as children, we might need extra support for a while as adults. This is especially the case when you are dealing with painful feelings and experiences.

People often feel ashamed of their need for support. They think they should be able to manage on their own, that there's something 'wrong' with them for needing to turn to others. It's horrid to feel like that. But there is nothing shameful about reaching out for support when you need it. It's actually part of being responsible and supporting yourself.

MY SUPPORT SYSTEMS

This exercise is to help you identify where you get support from and what may be missing or a bit thin. You can do it on paper (drawing or writing), or using a set of little objects.

Put yourself in the middle of the paper (or table/floor if you're using objects). Then put in around you any people or things in your life which support you. Think about anything or anybody which helps you keep going or helps you feel good in any way. Show people or things that feel very supportive close, and others further away.

When you have finished, look at what you have shown. Does it feel to you like there is enough there to support you, or do you wish there was more? Where are the gaps? Are there people you wish were closer (more present in your life or more supportive)? Do you need more people around, or different things from people? Do you need other things, like places to go out to, or a nicer environment?

If you identify that you need more of some sorts of support, you might feel upset. It is painful to feel what we need, but don't have. Sometimes it can feel like your needs are enormous. Perhaps it feels impossible or too scary to try to get the support you need.

When you are thinking about trying to get more support, it can be best to do it a small step at a time. Instead of thinking "I need more friends - oh, that's impossible!" you could think about how you could increase your support by one tiny bit. For example, can you think of one person you know and would like to try being a bit closer to? If so, could you decide to take a small risk about contacting them more often or sharing a little bit more about yourself with them?

REACHING OUT

If you need to reach out to new people, but are scared, again just try to do one very small thing at a time. This could be something like:

- Subscribe to a newsletter for people with your sorts of experiences or interests (see Resources at back).
- Find the number of a helpline, and give it a try.
- Find out about support groups - your local Mind organisation or Health Information service should be able to help.
- Get a penpal (perhaps through a newsletter).
- Go to a course on something like confidence-building or assertiveness at your local adult education centre. There are bound to be other people there who want to make new friends and are scared too.

THINGS TO REMIND YOURSELF OF

It's okay to need support. Everyone does.

If I get the support I need, I will be more able to support myself too. It will help me cope.

I might have to reach out for more support, but I can do that a tiny bit at a time.

IT'S YOUR LIFE

It is your precious life, to live for yourself, to do what's right for you. You may enjoy trying the next two ideas, which are about getting rid of old 'junk' you no longer want, and exploring your hopes and dreams for yourself.

THINGS I WANT TO GET RID OF

Get a cardboard box, which you can use as an imaginary chest or coffin. Into this, put things you want rid of - things that have made you feel bad. They could be actual objects or papers. Or they could be things to *represent* what has hurt or oppressed you - drawings, words written on paper, stones to represent the weights you have carried, and so on. Collect things over a period and put into the box. When you are ready, decide what to do with the box. Do you want to bury it, burn it, lock it away somewhere? Then make a ceremony of getting rid of it in your own way.

MY HOPES AND DREAMS

Having dreams for your life is the first step to making them happen. How do you want your life to be? Where would you like to live? What things would you like to do? How do *you* want to be? You could imagine your life one, two, five or ten years from now and make a picture of it, drawing or using pictures cut from magazines. You could write about it and talk to friends about it. Perhaps you can think of some small things you could do towards making your dreams for yourself into reality. Keep your dream-pictures somewhere safe. Add to them as you dream new hopes and dreams.

My journey

I've travelled in darkness for many years
cold and alone with my burden.
I've drifted and stumbled, blinded by pain
without hope of finding direction.

When the pain was too much I'd escape for a while
with the help of a blade, to oblivion.
I'd comfort myself and lighten my load
for the few short hours it lasted.

One day I knew I could journey no more,
the load had become unbearable.
The choice I then faced was to die in despair
or look at the load I was carrying.

I opened the pack, felt the pain, smelt the stench.
I didn't think I could bear it.
I steeled myself while I poked and I sorted
and reached for a hand to support me.

Amongst all the crap nearly hidden from view
what I found was a map and a compass.
And further down, a glimmer of light
that shone on the path to my future.

Y.

RESOURCES

Bristol Crisis Service for Women: Helpline and info on self-injury. PO Box 654 Bristol BS99 1XH. Tel. 0117 925 1119

Careline: Confidential counselling on any issue. Mon-Fri 10am-4pm. 0208 514 1177. Several Asian languages spoken.

Childline: For young people in trouble or danger. Freefone 0800 1111. 24 hours. Or write to Childline, Freepost 1111.

DABS: Free info on local support services for survivors. Sae to 4 New Hill, Conisbrough, Doncaster DN12 3HA 01302 768689.

Drinkline: alcohol problems Freefone: 0800 917 8282

Drugs: national helpline, 24 hours. Freefone: 0800 77 66 00

Eating Disorders Association: Information and support. Helpline 0845 634 1414 Youth helpline 0845 634 7650

Lesbian and Gay Switchboard 24-hour helpline:. 0207 837 7324.

MIND Info Line: Info on mental distress and treatment, incl. self-harm. 08457 660 163 (Local call rate). Mon-Fri 9.15-5.15.

National Self-harm Network: Information and campaigning for people who self-harm. PO Box 7264 Nottingham NG1 6WJ.

Refuge: Domestic violence helpline – counselling support and help for women & children. 24 hours. 0870 599 5443

Samaritans: 24-hour support (not just suicide). 08457 90 90 90.

Youth Access: Will put you in touch with young people's counselling & support projects in your area: 0208 772 9900.